THE UNIVERSE

PHOTO SELECTION AND TEXT BY
L. C. Casterline

BARNES
& NOBLE
BOOKS
NEW YORK

This edition published by

Barnes & Noble, Inc.,

by arrangement with Nancy Hall, Inc.

2005 Barnes & Noble Books

10 9 8 7 6 5 4 3 2 1

ISBN 0-7607-6608-8

Designed by Atif Toor and Nobue Shibuya

Images converted to stereo by Tim McCulloch

& Jenny Robinson, MAGroup, Bethel, CT

Printed in China

STARGAZING

As long as humans have been on Earth, they've been gazing up in wonder at the night sky. Eventually, they began recording their observations. Ancient cave paintings show that people saw pictures in the stars from the earliest times. In China, there is a record of a comet being sighted in 2296 B.C.E. The earliest known records of solar eclipses were made by the Chinese in 2136 B.C.E. and the Babylonians in 1223 B.C.E.

People all over the world saw and named patterns in the sky. Today, there are 88 officially recognized constellations.

Of course, just observing was not enough. Inevitably, people would want to explain the things they saw and use them to try and make sense of their world. The Babylonians, the ancient Egyptians, and many other peoples saw the Earth as a flat disk. The ancient Egyptians pictured the sky as the goddess Nut, her downward-facing body arched over Earth with her hands and feet defining north, south, east, and west. Each day, Nut gave birth to the Sun.

In Greece, Pythagoras theorized in the sixth century B.C.E. that the Earth was not flat, but a sphere that occupied the center of the universe with the Sun, the planets, and the stars revolving around it. Only one scholar did not agree with this view. In the fourth century B.C.E., Aristarchus proposed that Earth and the other planets orbited the Sun. No one believed him.

The next person to suggest a Sun-centered universe was Copernicus, whose work was published in 1543. Though the Copernican system was a simpler and more accurate way to calculate the movements of the planets, it was not regarded as reality.

Then in 1609, Galileo became the first person to use a telescope to view the stars and planets. Based on his observations, Galileo declared that the Copernicus was

Galileo

right. In 1633, under threat of torture and imprisonment by the Catholic church, Galileo was forced to recant his views. Nevertheless, his writings had been widely disseminated, and the Copernican theory was generally accepted by the end of the 1600s.

The 57-foot-long Lick refracting telescope, built in 1888, has a lens that is 36 inches across.

Galileo's refracting telescope used a lens to gather and focus light. Later in the 1600s, Sir Isaac Newton perfected a reflecting telescope, which used a mirror instead of a lens. Today, small telescopes are often refracting telescopes, while the large ones found in observatories are reflecting telescopes. Though it is easier to make big reflecting telescopes, the curve of the mirror must be exactly right in order for them to work well.

A radio telescope has a wide, curved surface that reflects radio waves to its central antenna.

Unfortunately, Earth-based optical telescopes are only good if the sky is clear and there isn't too much ambient light. In 1931, an American named Karl Jansky discovered that the center of the Milky Way Galaxy emitted radio waves. Six years later, Grote Reber built the first radio telescope in his backyard in Illinois. Unaffected by cloudy weather, radio telescopes can be huge, like the one in Arecibo, Puerto Rico, which has a 1,000-foot reflecting surface, or smaller ones can be clustered together, like the 27 radio telescopes of the Very Large Array in New Mexico.

In 1946, astrophysicist Lyman Spitzer, Jr., first suggested putting a large telescope in space. The first space telescope was launched in 1962 by Great Britain. More than 30 more would be launched before the Hubble Space Telescope was deployed by NASA in 1990. The Hubble uses an optical reflecting telescope, but there are also space observatories that gather

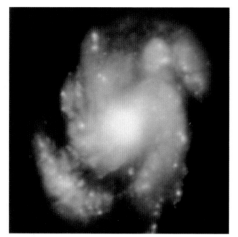

The Hubble Space Telescope's mirror was off by a fraction of a hair's width, yet it made a huge difference in the images it sent back to Earth before and after it was repaired (see page 16).

information from infrared light, X rays, gamma rays, and other forms of electromagnetic radiation. Unmanned space probes go far beyond Earth to send back images and information about the Sun and other planets. Some even travel beyond our solar system.

The Universe in 3-D contains some of the most spectacular NASA photographs. Usually, the type of 3-D effect used in this book is created with a stereo camera, which has two lenses set no more than 2.5 inches apart. This allows the photographer to take two photos at a time, each from a slightly different perspective. When the photographs are viewed through special lenses, the brain combines the two images into one 3-D image.

The Universe in 3-D, however, was made with photographs that already existed. To turn the images into stereo pairs, computer programs were used to separate each image into as many as 12 layers. Then each layer was examined to see which three would work together to make the best image.

THE IMAGES

ON THE WAY TO THE MOON

At 9:32 A.M. Eastern Daylight Time on July 16, 1969, the Apollo 11 Saturn V space vehicle lifted off from the John F. Kennedy Space Center in Cape Canaveral, Florida. Onboard were astronauts Neil A. Armstrong, Michael Collins, and Edwin E. "Buzz" Aldrin, Jr. Four days later, at 10:56 P.M. on July 20, Armstrong would make history by becoming the first person to set foot on the Moon. As he stepped off the ladder of the Lunar Module, he uttered the now famous words: "That's one small step for a man, one giant leap for mankind." Armstrong and Aldrin spent 21 hours on the Moon's surface. The next day, they lifted off in the Lunar Module and returned to the orbiting Command Module, where Collins was waiting. On July 24, the Command Module re-entered Earth's atmosphere and parachuted into the Pacific Ocean southwest of Hawaii, where they were picked up by the USS *Hornet*.

A VIEW OF HOMEHEADER

On July 20, 1969, astronauts Neil A. Armstrong and Edwin E. "Buzz" Aldrin, Jr., snapped a picture of faraway Earth as the Lunar Module, the *Eagle*, approached the surface of the Moon. As the ship touched down, Armstrong reported back to Earth, saying, "The *Eagle* has landed."

MISSION ACCOMPLISHED

While astronauts Neil A. Armstrong and Edwin E. "Buzz" Aldrin, Jr., were walking on the Moon, Michael Collins waited alone in the orbiting Command Module, the *Columbia*. Collins—and, seemingly, planet Earth—watched as the Lunar Module containing Armstrong and Aldrin lifted off the Moon's surface to return to the *Columbia*.

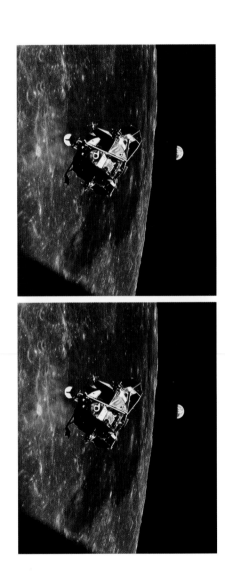

THE CHANDRA DEPLOYMENT MISSION

O n July 23, 1999, the space shuttle *Columbia* lifted off from the John F. Kennedy Space Center. Onboard were Commander Eileen M. Collins, Pilot Jeffrey S. Ashby, and Mission Specialists Steven A. Hawley, Catherine G. Coleman, and Michel Tognini of France. The mission was historic on two counts: It was the first time a woman served as commander of a shuttle mission, and the shuttle carried the 45-foot-long Chandra X-ray Observatory into orbit, the largest satellite ever launched by a shuttle. The Chandra is the world's most powerful X-ray telescope, producing pictures that are 25 times sharper than earlier X-ray images. With the Chandra, scientists can observe black holes, turbulent high-temperature gas clouds, supernovas, and dark matter, gaining new clues to the structure and evolution of the universe.

MAKING REPAIRS

The space shuttle *Endeavor* left Earth on December 2, 1993, to repair a mirror and make some adjustments on the Hubble Space Telescope (HST). Commander Richard O. Covey was accompanied by Pilot Kenneth D. Bowersox, Payload Commander F. Story Musgrave, and Mission Specialists Katherine C. Thornton, Claude Nicollier, Jeffrey A. Hoffman, and Thomas D. Akers. On December 4, Covey brought the *Endeavor* to within 30 feet of the HST and Nicollier used the shuttle's robot arm to capture and berth it in the ship's cargo bay. Later the same day, Musgrave and Hoffman made the first spacewalk, or EVA (Extra Vehicular Activity). Altogether, there would be five EVAs, more than on any previous mission. Eleven days after launch, the *Endeavor* returned to Earth, having successfully completed its mission.

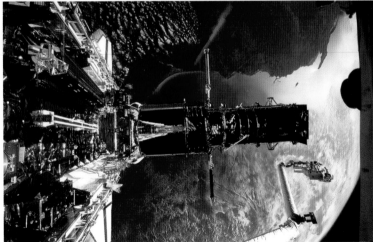

BETTER VISION

The *Discovery* space shuttle lifted off on February 11, 1997, with Commander Kenneth D. Bowersox, Pilot Scott J. Horowitz, and Mission Specialists Mark C. Lee, Steven A. Hawley, Gregory J. Harbaugh, Steven L. Smith, and Joseph R. Tanner aboard. The astronauts were on their way to equip the Hubble Space Telescope (HST) with two new cameras. The Near Infrared Camera and Multi-Object Spectrometer had improved infrared-light detectors, which would allow scientists to observe the most distant galaxies. The Space Telescope Imaging Spectrograph would provide a more detailed look at celestial objects and search for supermassive black holes. After installing the cameras and redeploying the HST at a higher altitude, the *Discovery* flew around it for one last look before returning to Earth on February 21.

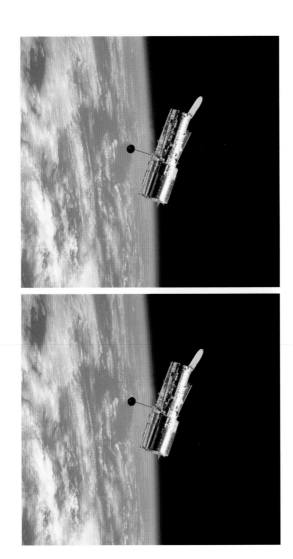

THE SOLAR SYSTEM

From the top, this montage of all the planets except Pluto shows Mercury, Venus, Earth (and the Moon), Mars, Jupiter, Saturn, Uranus, and Neptune. The size of the planets in each group—the top four rocky planets and the bottom four gas giants—are shown roughly to scale in relation to each other. *Mariner 10* took the image of Mercury; *Magellan*, the image of Venus; *Galileo*, the image of Earth; *Viking*, the image of Mars; and *Voyager*, the images of Jupiter, Saturn, Uranus, and Neptune.

VENUS

ava flows spread out for hundreds of miles from Maat Mons, a five-mile-high, active volcano on Venus. It is named after Maat, the ancient Egyptian goddess of truth, law, and justice. The image was created with radar altimetry data from the *Magellan* spacecraft. The viewpoint is from a mile above the surface of the planet and to the south of Maat Mons. The vertical scale is exaggerated 22.5 times. The simulated colors are based on the color images recorded by the Soviet spacecraft *Venera 13* and *14*, which landed on Venus in March 1982. The *Venera 13* survived the longest, lasting for two hours and seven minutes in a temperature of 854.6 degrees Fahrenheit and under a pressure equaling 84 Earth atmospheres.

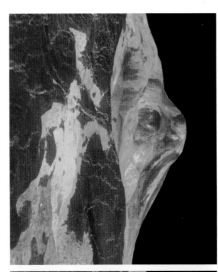

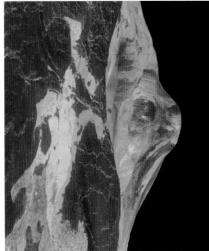

MARS

The *Mars Pathfinder* landed in the Ares Vallis region of Mars on July 4, 1997. The photograph shows a section of a 360-degree panorama taken by the Imager for Mars Pathfinder (IMP) over the course of three Martian days. The IMP is a stereo imaging system that stands six feet above the surface of the planet. In the foreground, part of the lander is visible with the ramp used by the *Sojourner* rover fully extended. Tracks lead from the ramp to *Sojourner*, which is using its Alpha Proton X-ray Spectrometer to study a large rock nicknamed "Yogi," which is similar to basalt. In the background at left are two hills called the "Twin Peaks."

J upiter is the largest planet. Here, it is shown with its four largest moons, which are known as the Galilean Satellites. Starting from the top, the moons are Io, Europa, Ganymede, and Callisto. Ganymede is the largest moon in the entire solar system, while Europa is about the same size as Earth's Moon. The Great Red Spot visible on Jupiter's surface is a gigantic storm that was first observed about 300 years ago. The storm is more than 7,900 miles long from north to south and twice that from east to west. Its winds spin counterclockwise at roughly 250 miles per hour. The *Galileo* spacecraft took the images of Jupiter, Io, and Ganymede in June 1996 and the image of Europa in September of the same year. The image of Callisto was taken by the *Voyager 1* spacecraft in 1979.

SATURN

n 1610, Galileo looked at Saturn through his 20x telescope and thought he saw a three-bodied planet. In 1655, Christiaan Huygens suggested that Saturn was surrounded by a solid ring. Now we know that the planet has seven major rings, which are made up of thousands of smaller ones. The rings are composed mostly of ice chunks and range from tiny particles to boulder-sized. The planet also has 33 moons, including two that were discovered in 2004. In this photo montage created by assembling images taken by the *Voyager 1* spacecraft in 1980, Dione looms in the foreground, with Saturn behind it. Enceladus and Rhea can be seen on the upper left, Tethys and Mimas at bottom right, and Titan, its largest moon, at top right. The cloud-covered Titan is the second largest moon in the solar system and is larger than the planets Mercury and Pluto, while Saturn's smallest moon is only two miles in diameter.

URANUS

Until March 1977, Saturn was thought to be the only planet with rings. Then Earth-based observers watching the occultation of a star by Uranus, noticed that the star blinked out five times before and after it was blocked by the planet. This suggested that Uranus was encircled by five rings. Later observations, including those made by the *Voyager 2* spacecraft, which flew by the planet in 1986, and the Keck II telescope in Hawaii indicate that altogether there are nine major rings and two minor ones. In this false color image created with 1998 data from the Hubble Space Telescope's Near Infrared Camera and Multi-Object Spectrometer, two of the rings are visible, along with several of Uranus's 27 moons. Bright clouds, probably made up of methane crystals, can be seen in the planet's northern hemisphere. The light spot above the southern polar area is a high-altitude haze. Uranus is the only planet that is tipped on its side, possibly the result of a long-ago collision with another planet-sized body.

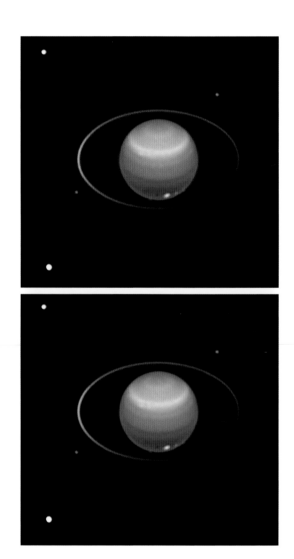

NEPTUNE

Though they are not visible in this composite photograph created from a *Voyager* image, Neptune has seven faint rings that probably consist of rock and dust. In the foreground is Triton, the largest of its 13 known moons, and the only large moon in the solar system rotating in the opposite direction of its planet's rotation. This leads scientists to believe that the moon may have come from somewhere else in the solar system and been captured by Neptune's gravitational field. The temperature at Triton's surface, which is mainly nitrogen ice, is about minus 391 degrees Fahrenheit, making it the coldest known surface in the solar system. Triton also has active cryogenic, or ice, volcanoes. The Earth-sized storm called the Great Dark Spot is visible on Neptune's surface. Nearby winds blow up to about 1,200 miles per hour.

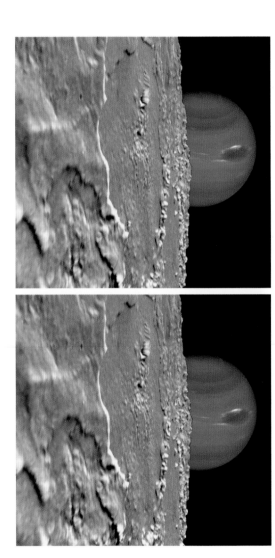

THE SUN

The Sun is a roiling mass of gases. What we see as the surface is really a thick layer of gases called the photosphere, where temperatures average about 10,000 degrees Fahrenheit. This is where we see sunspots, regions with strong magnetic fields and lower temperatures than the surrounding gases. Above the photosphere is an irregular layer of gases called the chromosphere. Here, temperatures range from just over 10,000 degrees Fahrenheit near the photosphere to about 36,000 degrees in the upper regions. Clouds of hot gases suspended above the photosphere by magnetic fields are called prominences. Occasionally, they erupt and escape the Sun's atmosphere. A huge prominence is visible on the upper right of this image of the Sun taken on September 14, 1999, by an Extreme Ultraviolet Imaging Telescope. The white areas are the hottest regions, while the dark red areas are the coolest.

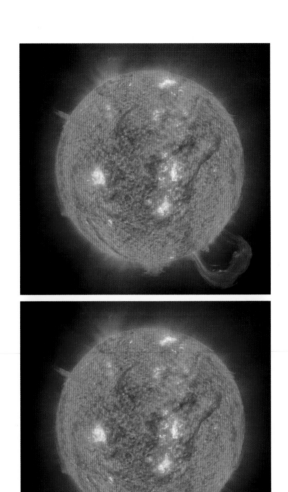

THE SAGITTARIUS STAR CLOUD

n this spectacular photograph taken by the Hubble Space Telescope in 2002, thousands of multicolored stars are sprinkled against the black velvet sky like sparkling jewels. The different colors of stars are due to their surface temperature. The fainter orange or red stars are similar to our Sun. Stars that are younger, larger, and hotter appear blue or greenish. The bright red stars are red giants, stars that were once like our Sun but are now older and cooler because they are running out of fuel. The Sagittarius Star Cloud is a narrow dust-free area that allows us a glimpse of some of the oldest known stars near the center of our own Milky Way Galaxy.

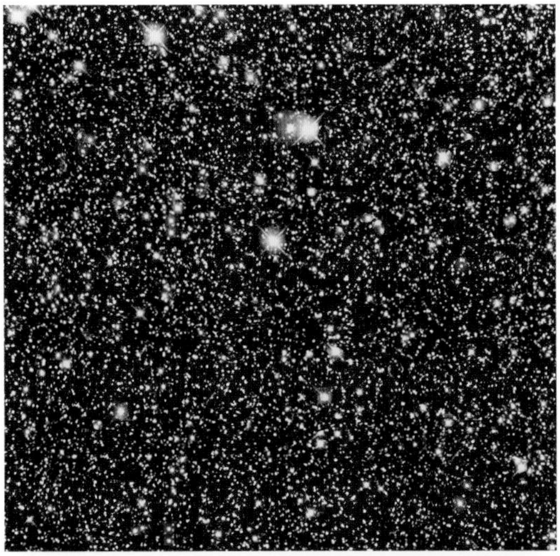

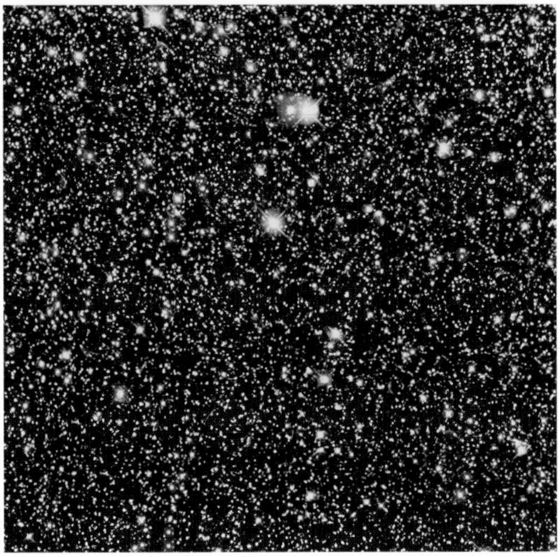

A CELESTIAL ZOOM LENS

Abell 2218 is an enormous cluster of galaxies about two billion light-years away from Earth. The cluster is so huge that its gravitational field acts something like an optical lens, bending light rays that pass through it. Called gravitational lensing, this phenomenon magnifies images of distant objects beyond the cluster, allowing scientists to study remote galaxies that even the largest telescopes could not otherwise detect. These galaxies, which are five to ten times more distant than the cluster, appear as arcs in this photograph taken by the Hubble Space Telescope. The galaxies are not only distant but also ancient, existing when the universe was only one-fourth its current age.

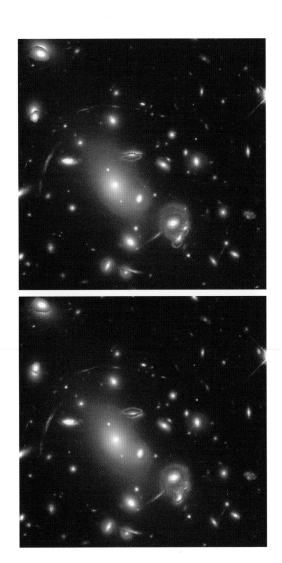

DANCING IN THE DARK

The four galaxies in the Hickson Compact Group 87 (HCG 87) appear to be performing a dance, albeit one that takes place over hundreds of millions of years. The dance is caused by the gravitational field of each galaxy acting upon the others. The largest galaxy in the group, HCG 87a at bottom, is seen from the side but is actually disk-shaped. Both HCG 87a and HCG 87b, the bright-centered galaxy at its right, are thought to have black holes at their center. In HCG 87c, the larger spiral galaxy at top left, new stars may be forming. It is not certain whether the smaller spiral galaxy in the center is really part of the group or a more distant, unrelated galaxy.

THE WHIRLPOOL GALAXY

This view of the nearby galaxy M51, also known as the Whirlpool Galaxy, was composed from images and data taken by the Hubble Space Telescope (HST) and researchers at the Kitt Peak National Observatory in Tucson, Arizona. The gravitational pull of a companion galaxy, NGC 5195, has caused young, energetic stars to form in the spiraling arms of M51. The light from emissions of hot, glowing hydrogen gives the clusters of new stars their bright red color. Details caught by the HST's Wide Field and Planetary Camera 2 have even allowed scientists to associate the young star clusters with their parent dust and gas clouds.

A STARBURST RING

The barred spiral galaxy NGC 1512 is circled by a ring of new star clusters that is 2,400 light-years wide. Some of the new star clusters are hidden in glowing red parent clouds of dust and gas. Others are almost completely visible as bright blue clumps, their parent clouds cleared away by the powerful radiation emissions and stellar winds of the young stars. Three different cameras in the Hubble Space Telescope—the Faint Object Camera, the Wide Field and Planetary Camera 2, and the Near Infrared Camera and Multi-Object Spectrometer—were used to take the seven images employed to create this color-composite photograph. Though NGC 1512 is a barred spiral galaxy, the bar cannot be seen in this photograph.

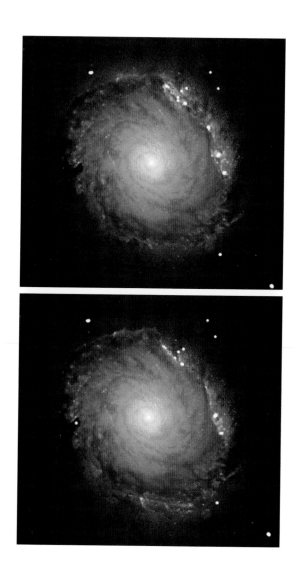

CLOSE ENCOUNTERS

C omputer simulations show that the smaller IC 2163 galaxy at right is swinging by the much larger galaxy NGC 2207 in a counterclockwise direction. The two spiral galaxies were at their closest about 40 million years ago. Though the danger of colliding would seem to be past, IC 2163 doesn't have enough energy to escape the gravitational field of NGC 2207. Sometime in the future, it will be pulled back toward the larger galaxy. After continuing to circle each other for billions of years, the two galaxies will merge and become one massive galaxy. The long streamers of gas and stars stretching hundreds of thousands of miles to the right of IC 2163 are the result of distortion caused by its current close encounter with NGC 2207.

TWISTED

When viewed from the side, spiral galaxies appear to be flat, but that's not the case with the ESO 510-G13 galaxy. Instead, ESO 510-G13 appears to be warped. Scientists think the warping was caused by a collision with another galaxy that took place less than a billion years ago. It's believed that the disk will eventually straighten out and appear to be flat. Images taken with three color filters (red, blue, and green) by The Hubble Space Telescope Wide Field and Planetary Camera 2 were used to create this composite image.

THE BLACK EYE GALAXY

The Messier 64 (M64) galaxy was independently discovered by three different people within a year: Edward Piggot on March 23, 1779, Johann Elert Bode on April 4, 1779, and Charles Messier on March 1, 1780. Messier was the first to catalog this spiral galaxy, and so it bears his name. Its nickname, the "Black Eye Galaxy," comes from the dark band of dust in front of its bright core. M64 is about 17 million light-years away from Earth. Though its stars and the gases in its inner regions rotate clockwise, as in most galaxies, the gases in M64's outer regions rotate in the opposite direction. This has led scientists to think the outer gases are from another galaxy that collided and merged with M64 about a billion years ago.

OVERLAPPING GALAXIES

NGC 3314 is actually two spiral galaxies about 25 million light-years apart. The smaller and closer NGC 3314a is seen face-on, silhouetted against the larger, more distant NGC 3314b. This unusual line-up allows astronomers to view dark material in the front galaxy, which would not otherwise be visible. The bright blue star clusters in NGC 3314a were recently formed from interstellar gas and dust. The reddish orange area just below the bright central cluster is the core of NGC 3314b showing through. Interstellar dust particles in NGC 3314a act in a similar way to particles in Earth's atmosphere, making the core of the more distant galaxy appear reddish orange, like the setting Sun. This composite image was created using archival images taken in 1999 with the Hubble Space Telescope's Wide Field and Planetary Camera 2 and newer images taken in 2000.

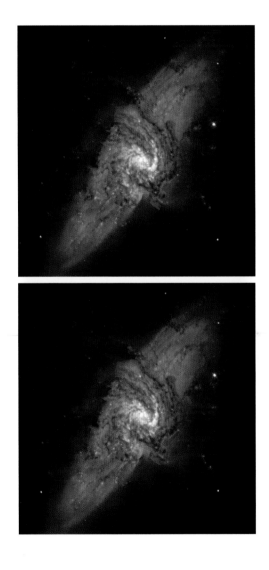

A FIERY MEETING

The NGC 4038 and NGC 4039 spiral galaxies are known as the Antennae Galaxies. They have been in the process of merging for the last 800 million years. The core of each galaxy shows up as a bright yellowy-white area, one above the other. The blue and green colors indicate stars in the galaxies, while the red areas show bursts of star formation triggered by the collision. The most intense area of activity is the bright red area where the galaxies overlap. This false-color composite image combines infrared light data from the Spitzer Space Telescope, which was launched on August 25, 2003, and visible light data from the Kitt Peak National Observatory in Tucson, Arizona.

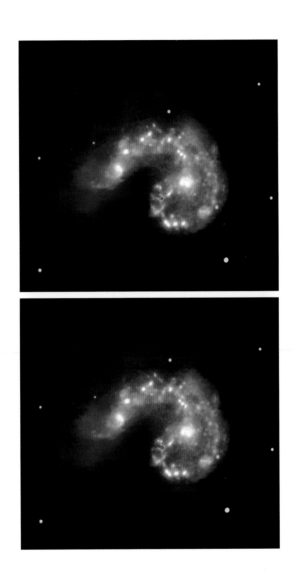

DWARF GALAXY

There are more dwarf galaxies in the universe than any other kind. NGC 1569 is a small, irregular-shaped dwarf galaxy only seven million light-years away from Earth. Just because it's small, however, doesn't mean it's quiet. About 25 million years ago, the galaxy was lit up by supernova explosions and star birth activity. The hydrogen gas bubbles caused by star birth glow reddish orange from the strong winds and radiation emitted from the hot young stars. This image taken by the Hubble Space Telescope is about 1,500 light-years across.

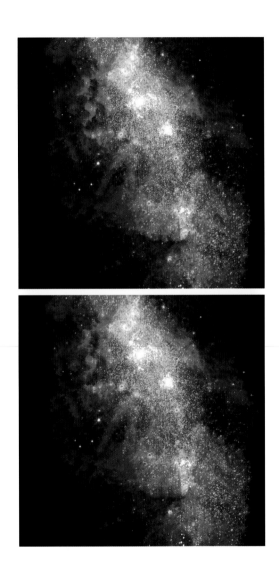

FROM BEGINNING TO END

Taken with the Hubble Space Telescope's Wide Field and Planetary Camera 2 on March 5, 1999, this amazing true-color picture of the largest region of glowing gas in the Milky Way Galaxy illustrates some of the stages in a star's life. Stars begin in glowing clouds of hydrogen like those seen on the right. At the center is a bright blue cluster of hot young stars. The cluster's fierce winds and ultraviolet radiation have cleared a space for itself in the hydrogen clouds. Slightly to the left and above the star cluster is Sher 25, a star that is nearing the end of its life. Encircled by a grayish blue ring, this blue supergiant is flanked by outflows of gas that appear as two blue blobs. It's likely that Sher 25 will explode in a spectacular supernova within the next few thousand years.

THE EAGLE NEBULA

One of the most famous pictures constructed from images taken by the Hubble Space Telescope's Wide Field and Planetary Camera 2 shows the immense gas and dust pillars that are part of the star-forming M16 nebula, also known as the Eagle Nebula. The pillars and their ghostly streamers are lit by ultraviolet light given off by nearby clusters of young stars. The tallest pillar is about one light-year long from base to top.

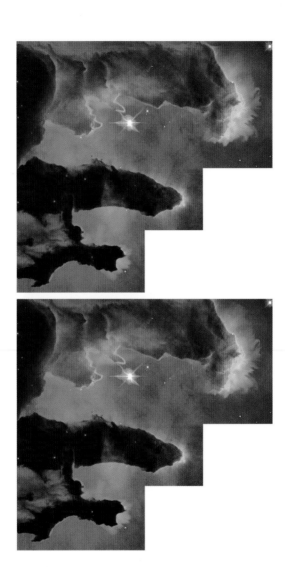

THACKERAY'S GLOBULES

The dense, dark clouds of gas and dust known as "globules" were first discovered in the IC 2944 nebula by A. D. Thackeray, an astronomer from South Africa, in 1950.

Little is known about the globules except that they are associated with star-forming areas called HII regions because of the presence of ionized hydrogen gas. The largest globule in the upper part of the image is actually two overlapping clouds, which are each about 1.5 light-years in length. The globules are in constant motion, possibly caused by the ultraviolet radiation from the hot, massive Type O stars that light up the gas and dust of IC 2944. This composite picture was created by combining images taken by the Hubble Space Telescope's Wide Field and Planetary Camera 2 in 1999 with additional broadband images taken in 2001.

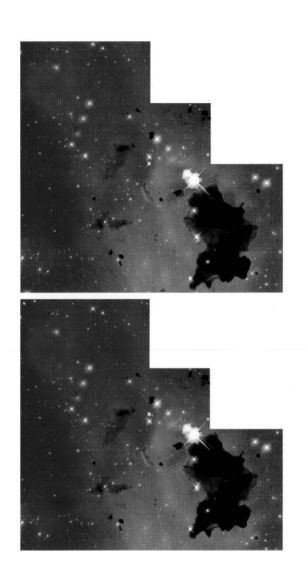

EMBRYOS OF THE STARS

The giant cloud of gas and dust called the Trifid Nebula (NGC 6514) is roughly 5,400 light-years away in the constellation Sagittarius. It has four relatively cold dust "cocoons" that serve as star incubators. Until January 2005, astronomers did not think stars had begun to form in them. Then, the Spitzer Space Telescope probed the cocoons with its Infrared Array Camera and detected 30 rapidly growing stellar embryos about to burst into new stars. It also found about 120 small stars inside the outer clouds of the nebula. These were probably formed at the same time and from the same cloud of dust as the massive Type O star at the nebula's center. Type O stars are the biggest stars in the universe. In astronomical time, they don't last very long, but they go out with a bang as supernovas.

WHEN A ROSE IS NOT A ROSE

The small NGC 7129 nebula, which is the color and shape of a rosebud, is just 3,300 light-years away from Earth. This image taken by the Spitzer Space Telescope's Infrared Array Camera in February 2004 covers an area that is about one-fourth the size of our full Moon. There are about 130 young stars clustered in the nebula, which contains enough stellar materials to create about 1,000 Sunlike stars. It took a million years for the young stars to blow the large rosebud-shaped bubble in the cloud of gas and dust that had once enveloped them like a cocoon. Astronomers think that our Sun may have developed in a similar star cluster billions of years ago.

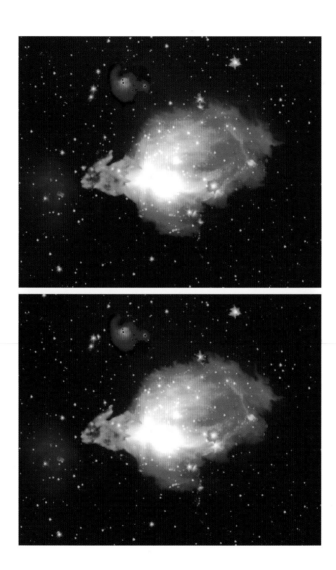

A DISTANT STAR NURSERY

Though the NGC 604 nebula is in a spiral galaxy about 2.7 million light-years distant from Earth, it is so huge it can be seen through Earth-based telescopes. Almost 1,500 light-years in diameter, the nebula contains more than 200 hot young stars, which range from 15 to 60 times the size of our Sun. Heat from these massive stars lights up the gaseous walls of the giant nebula, highlighting its three-dimensional structure. This picture of NGC 604 was compiled from images using different light filters taken by the Hubble Space Telescope's Wide Field and Planetary Camera 2 in January 1995.

HERBIG-HARO OBJECTS

The gravity of a young star, such as the central star in this image, often attracts disks of dust and gas from its surrounding nebula. This material spirals in toward the star and some of it increases the star's mass. However, a fraction of the gas is ejected at right angles to the star at a speed of almost 200 miles per second. As these jets of gas drive into the nebula, their strong shock waves heat the gas, causing it to glow in the light of the star. This glow is called a Herbig-Haro object, after astronomers George Herbig and Guillermo Haro, who did early work in this area in the 1950s. The bright jet of gas at the top is headed roughly in Earth's direction. The jet going in the opposite direction, which can be seen just to the lower right of the star, appears much fainter, perhaps because of obscuring dust.

BLOWING BUBBLES

N GC 7635, also known as the Bubble Nebula, was formed by fast-moving stellar winds of ionized gas produced by the massive star BD+602522, which can be seen at left within the bubble. As the gas from the star expands, it pushes the sparse gas surrounding it into a shell, which glows from the light of the star. The bubble is about six light-years across and more than 11,000 light-years away from Earth, toward the constellation Cassiopeia.

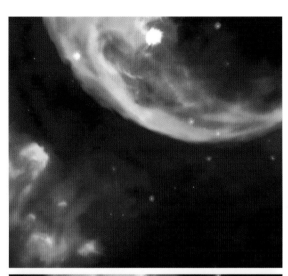

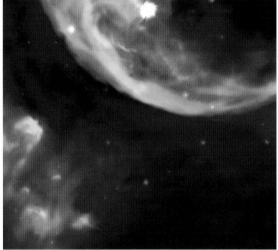

COSMIC TORNADOES

About 5,000 light-years away from Earth, in the Lagoon Nebula (M8), are a pair of funnel-shaped clouds that are billions of miles long. The tornado-like appearance of the clouds may be caused by wind shear created by the temperature differences between their hot surfaces and cold interiors. The brightest region of the nebula, called the Hourglass, is lit by radiation from the central hot star O Herschel 36, which can be seen shining on the lower right. The individual images combined to produce this image were taken by the Hubble Space Telescope's Wide Field and Planetary Camera 2 in July and September 1995.

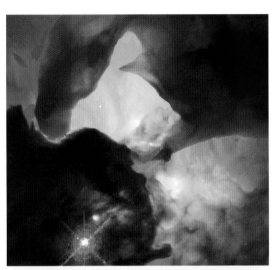

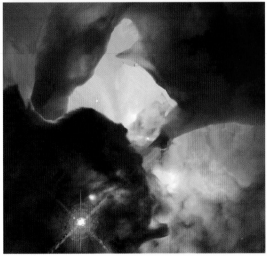

DEATH OF A SUN-SIZED STAR

When stars the size of our Sun die, they violently eject most of their material as gas and dust. In this image taken by the Hubble Space Telescope's Wide Field and Planetary Camera 2, the dying star is hidden in the dusty central "belt." To either side, bright yellow jets of gas containing most of the star's matter streak away at speeds of up to one million miles per hour. The high speed of the gas jets causes shock fronts to form on impact, heating interstellar gases, which can be seen in blue. Eventually, the gas and dust from the dying star will form a planetary nebula. Astronomers have already named the more than eight-trillion-mile-long structure the Calabash Nebula (OH231.8+4.2). It is also called the Rotten Egg Nebula because its sulfur content would give off a hideous odor—that is, if one could smell anything in space.

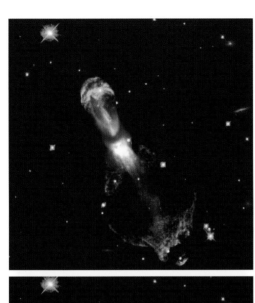

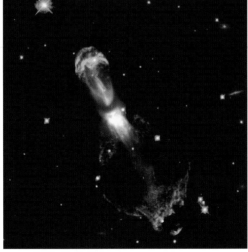

THE CAT'S EYE NEBULA

The beautiful young planetary nebula NGC 6543, also known as the Cat's Eye Nebula, is a complex structure of concentric gas shells, high-speed gas jets, and shock-induced gas knots. This has led astronomers to suspect the nebula may be the result of a pair of dying stars that are too close together to be distinguished. About 3,000 light-years from Earth, NGC 6543 is only about 1,000 years old. Though the "cocoons" that are formed by the outer layers of gas from dying stars are called planetary nebulas, they are not true star-forming nebulas.

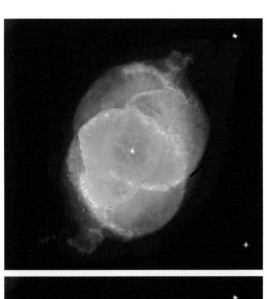

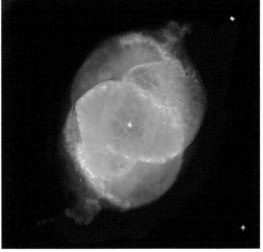

THE ANT NEBULA

When viewed from Earth-based telescopes, the Mz3 planetary nebula looks like the head and thorax of an ant, resulting in its nickname, the Ant Nebula.

The much higher resolution of images taken by the Hubble Space Telescope's Wide Field and Planetary Camera 2 in 1998 reveals two fiery lobes of gas billowing outward from the dying star in the center. The symmetrical patterns of the gas lobes may be caused by the gravitational pull of a closely orbiting companion star, which could have been swallowed by the formerly Sun-sized dying star. The other possibility is that they've been wound into complex shapes by the strong magnetic field of the spinning star.

MASSIVE SELF-DESTRUCTION

On February 23, 1987, astronomers witnessed the spectacular self-destruction of a massive star that actually took place about 165 thousand years B.C.E. in the Large Magellanic Cloud, roughly 167,000 light-years from Earth. The debris from the explosion of supernova 1987a is moving outward at speeds of almost six million miles per hour. This image, taken in 1994 by the Hubble Space Telescope's Wide Field and Planetary Camera 2, shows the three glowing gas rings that encircle the supernova.

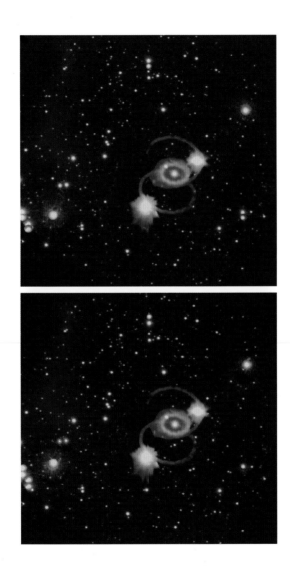

SUPERSIZED SHOCK WAVE

This picture created from images taken in three different colors by the Hubble Space Telescope in 1993, shows a small section of the shock wave from supernova NGC 6960/95 that occurred in the constellation Cygnus about 15,000 years ago.

Known as the Cygnus Loop, the supernova remnant stretches out over a distance about six times the diameter of Earth's Moon and is about 2,600 light-years from Earth. The shock wave has slowed after colliding with a cloud of interstellar gas, allowing a high-speed knot of gas (the blue streak) possibly ejected by the supernova to catch up with it.

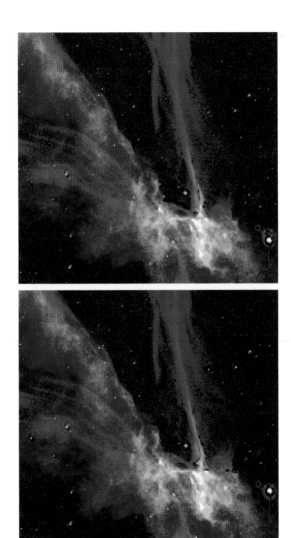

AN INVISIBLE STAR

Filaments of gas in the supernova N49 remnant seem to pirouette before an audience of glittering stars in this composite picture based on images taken by the Hubble Space Telescope's Wide Field and Planetary Camera 2 in 2000. Though the light from the supernova reached Earth thousands of years ago, gamma-ray detectors on nine spacecraft detected an intense burst of radiation coming from the remnant on March 25, 1979. Though the burst lasted just two-tenths of a second, it released as much energy as the Sun does in 1,000 years. When massive stars explode in a supernova explosion, they usually leave neutron stars, which eventually become pulsars. Astronomers have wondered why the nebulas created by many supernovas don't have pulsars. After studying N49 and two other remnants with similar gamma-ray bursts, astronomers deduced the presence of a magnetar, a spinning neutron star with an enormously powerful magnetic field that causes starquakes, which are the source of the gamma-ray bursts.

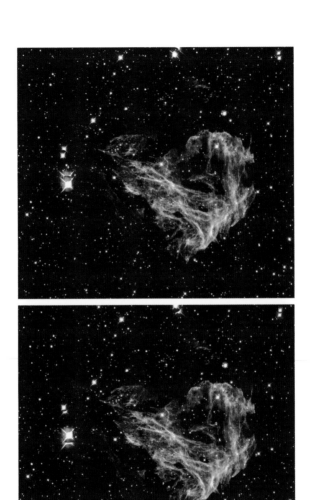

GLOSSARY

barred spiral galaxy   A flattened galaxy whose arms arc out in opposite directions from the ends of a central bar of stars, gas, and dust.

black hole   The incredibly dense, collapsed core that may be left after a massive star explodes in a supernova. The gravity of a black hole is so strong that even light, which travels at about 186,000 miles per second, cannot escape it.

blue supergiant   The stage of a massive dying star after it has progressed from red giant to red supergiant and lost its extended atmosphere, becoming smaller and much hotter.

Chandra X-ray Observatory   A 45-foot-long satellite containing the most powerful X-ray telescope in the world. Launched in 1999, the Chandra is in an elliptical orbit around Earth at altitudes ranging from almost 10,000 miles to more than 82,000 miles, traveling at speeds up to about 10,490 miles per hour. The Chandra is named after the Indian-American astrophysicist Subrahmanyan Chandrasekhar (1910–1995).

chromosphere   The area of the Sun's (or any other star's) atmosphere that lies between the photosphere and the corona. The temperature of the Sun's chromosphere ranges from just over 10,000 degrees Fahrenheit in lower areas to about 36,000 degrees in the upper regions.

constellation   A group of stars that forms a pattern in the sky. There are 88 officially recognized star patterns.

corona   The top level of the Sun's atmosphere, whose temperatures can reach over seven million degrees Fahrenheit. Without special equipment, the corona can only be seen during a total eclipse.

cryogenic volcano   A volcano that spews molten ice or ice fragments.

dark matter   Material that cannot be detected by telescopes but is inferred to exist from the movement of galaxies, which seem to be bound by the gravity of more matter than is visible.

dust   Microscopic particles of matter in space.

dwarf galaxy   A small, faint galaxy.

electromagnetic radiation   Energy in the form of photons (particles that have no mass) that travel at the speed of light in waves of various lengths. The types of electromagnetic radiation, ranging from the most energetic with the shortest wavelength to the least energetic with the longest wavelength are gamma rays, X rays, ultraviolet light, visible light, infrared light, microwaves, and radio waves.

Extra Vehicular Activity (EVA)   When an astronaut ventures outside a spacecraft or space station that is either orbiting Earth or has landed on the Moon; also called a spacewalk or moonwalk.

galaxy   A large cluster of stars ranging in size from a few million to several trillion, accompanied by interstellar gas, dust, and possibly dark matter.

Galilean Satellites   Io, Europa, Ganymede, and Callisto, Jupiter's four largest moons, which were discovered by Galileo Galilei in 1610.

gamma rays   The most energetic type of electromagnetic radiation with the shortest wavelength.

gas giant   A large planet that has a rocky core but consists mainly of hydrogen and helium, along with other substances, such as methane and ammonia.

gravitational field   The area of space affected by the gravity of a galaxy, star, planet, or other celestial object.

gravitational lensing   A focusing effect caused by the gravity of a large intervening celestial object, such as a galaxy, that bends and magnifies the light coming from a more distant galaxy that could not otherwise be seen.

gravity   A physical force by which one celestial object with mass attracts another.

Great Dark Spot   An Earth-sized storm in Neptune's southern hemisphere.

Great Red Spot   A gigantic storm more than 7,900 miles long and 15,800 miles wide in Jupiter's southern hemisphere.

Herbig-Haro object   The glow caused by heat from shock waves when jets of gas ejected by a young star collide with the parent nebula.

HII region   Star-forming areas that get their name from the presence of ionized hydrogen gas, the symbol for which is HII.

Hubble Space Telescope (HST)   The first space-based observatory, which was launched in 1990. The HST is 43.5 feet long and orbits Earth at an altitude of about 353 miles, traveling 17,500 miles per hour. Its scientific instruments include the Wild Field and Planetary Camera 2, the Near Infrared Camera and Multi-Object Spectrometer, the Space Telescope Imaging Spectrograph, and the Advanced Camera for Surveys. It is named after American astronomer Edwin P. Hubble (1889–1953).

infrared light   The type of electromagnetic radiation that falls between visible light and microwaves.

ionized gas   Atoms of gas that have a positive electrical charge caused by the loss of one or more electrons.

irregular galaxy   A galaxy that does not have a defined shape or structure.

light-year   The distance that light travels in one year at a rate of about 186,000 miles per second, or about 5.88 trillion miles.

magnetar   A spinning neutron star with a magnetic field that is trillions of times stronger than Earth's.

magnetic field   The area of space affected by the magnetic forces of a galaxy, star, planet, or other celestial object.

Milky Way Galaxy   The spiral galaxy that contains our solar system. Formed about 14 billion years ago, the Milky Way Galaxy is about 100,000 light-years in diameter and contains about 100 billion stars.

mons   A mountain.

moon   A natural satellite that orbits a planet.

nebula   A cloud of interstellar dust and gas.

neutron star   The extremely dense, collapsed core that may be left after a massive star explodes in a supernova. A neutron star equal to 1.4 to 3 solar masses will not collapse any further. If the core is more than 3 solar masses, however, a black hole will form.

occultation   The blockage of light of one celestial object by another.

orbit   The curved path of one object as it moves around another object, whose gravity keeps the orbiting object from flying off into space.

photosphere   The thick layer of gases we see as the "surface" of the Sun, where temperatures average just over 10,000 degrees Fahrenheit.

planetary nebula   The cloud of gas and dust formed by a dying Sun-sized star.

prominence   A cloud of hot gases suspended above the Sun's photosphere by magnetic fields. Prominences sometimes erupt, escaping the Sun's atmosphere.

pulsar   A rapidly spinning young neutron star that produces regular pulses of radiation.

radar   A way to use radio waves to detect, locate, and track objects and to measure their distance and altitude; also, the equipment used to do so.

radar altimetry   A method of using radar signals to measure the distance between an orbiting spacecraft and a point on the surface of a planet.

radiation   Energy that travels in the form of waves or particles.

red giant   The stage in a dying star's life when it has exhausted its hydrogen supply, its core has shrunk, and its outer layers have expanded and cooled. Red giants formed by massive stars are called red supergiants.

retrograde   The clockwise rotation of a planet or other celestial object when viewed from above its north pole.

rocky planet   A small planet consisting mostly of rock.

rover   A vehicle used to explore the surface of a celestial body, such as the Moon or Mars.

satellite   A natural or manmade object that orbits a larger object.

solar system   A star and all the natural objects that orbit it.

space   The airless region of the universe beyond the limits of Earth's atmosphere, and through which all celestial bodies travel.

space shuttle   A NASA spacecraft that can be used to carry people and cargo into orbit around Earth, then return to Earth and be used again.

spacewalk   When an astronaut ventures outside a spacecraft or space station that is either orbiting Earth or has landed on the Moon; also called Extra Vehicular Activity (EVA).

spectrometer   An instrument used to separate and measure different wavelengths of electromagnetic radiation.

spiral galaxy   A flattened galaxy whose arms spiral out from a dense central core.

Spitzer Space Telescope (SST)   A large space observatory launched in 2003. Instead of orbiting Earth, the SST trails Earth in its orbit around the Sun. Its imaging systems are the Multiband Imaging Photometer, the Infrared Array Camera, and the Infrared Spectrograph. The SST is named after the American astrophysicist Lyman Spitzer, Jr. (1914–1997).

star   A celestial ball of gas with enough mass to be so compressed by its own gravity that it produces internal nuclear fusion reactions.

star cluster   A group of stars that formed from the same cloud of gas and dust and are bound together by gravity.

stellar wind   The gases that continually flow from the surface of a star into space.

sunspot   An area of the Sun's photosphere that has a strong magnetic field and appears dark because its temperatures are lower than the surrounding photosphere.

supernova   The last stage of a dying massive star, when the star explodes, and its core collapses, forming a neutron star or a black hole. A supernova can be a billion times brighter than the Sun.

supernova remnant   The gases that remain after a star has exploded as a supernova.

telescope   An instrument used to collect and magnify visible light or other forms of electromagnetic radiation from distant objects.

Thackeray's Globules   Relatively small, dense clouds of dust and gas that appear as black blobs when viewed against a glowing nebula. Some scientists believe that Thackeray's Globules are the first stage of star birth.

ultraviolet light   The type of electromagnetic radiation that falls between X rays and visible light.

universe   Everything that exists in space, including cosmic dust and gas, meteoroids, asteroids, comets, moons, planets, stars, black holes, and dark matter.

wind shear   A sudden, extreme change in wind speed or direction or both over a relatively short distance

X ray   The type of electromagnetic radiation that falls between gamma rays and microwaves.

INDEX

pp. 3, 4: Library of Congress

p. 5: Ablestock

pp. 9, 11, 13, 15: NASA Kennedy Space Center (NASA-KSC)

p. 17: NASA Marshall Space Flight Center (NASA-MSFC)

p. 19: NASA Headquarters—Greatest Images of NASA (NASA-HQ-GRIN)

pp. 21, 23, 25, 27, 29, 31, 33, 35: NASA Jet Propulsion Laboratory (NASA-JPL)

p. 39: NASA/A. Fruchter and the ERO Team (STScI, ST-ECF)

pp. 6, 45, 83: NASA Goddard Space Flight Center (NASA-GSFC)

pp. 37, 41, 47, 53, 71, 73: NASA/The Hubble Heritage Team (STScI/AURA)

p. 43: NASA/The Hubble Heritage Team (STScI/AURA)/N. Scoville (Caltech) and T. Rector (NOAO)

p. 49: NASA/The Hubble Heritage Team (STScI/AURA)/C. Conselice (University of Wisconsin/STScI)

p. 51: NASA/The Hubble Heritage Team (STScI/AURA)/S. Smartt (Institute of Astronomy) and D. Richstone (University of Michigan)

p. 55: NASA/JPL-Caltech/Z. Wang (Harvard-Smithsonian CfA)

p. 57: NASA/ESA/P. Anders (Göttingen University, Germany)

p. 59: NASA/Wolfgang Brandner (JPL-IPAC), Eva K. Grebel (University of Washington), You-Hua Chu (University of Illinois, Urbana-Champaign)

p. 61: NASA/Jeff Hester and Paul Scowen (Arizona State University)

p. 63: NASA/The Hubble Heritage Team (STScI/AURA)/Bo Reipurth (University of Hawaii)

p. 65: NASA/JPL-Caltech/J. Rho (SSC/Caltech)

p. 67: NASA/JPL-Caltech/T. Megeath (Harvard-Smithsonian CfA)

p. 69: NASA/Hui Yang (University of Illinois)

p. 75: NASA/A. Caulet (St-ECF, ESA)

p. 77: NASA/ESA/Valentin Bujarrabal (Observatorio Astronómico Nacional, Spain)

p. 79: NASA/J. P. Harrington and K. J. Borkowski (University of Maryland)

p. 81: NASA/The Hubble Heritage Team (STScI/AURA)/R. Sahai (Jet Propulsion Lab) and B. Balick (University of Washington)

p. 85: NASA/J. J. Hester (Arizona State University)

p. 87: NASA/The Hubble Heritage Team (STScI/AURA)/Y. Chu (University of Illinois, Urbana-Champaign)